A GOLDEN BOOK • NEW YORK

KOHL'S
Style 18034
Factory Number 126509
Production Date 01/2020

Ages 3 and up

MANUFACTURED IN CHINA
10 9 8 7 6 5 4 3 2 1

How Do Lions Say I Love You?

Diane Muldrow ♥ Illustrated by David Walker

A hen says *I love you*
to her chicks with a cluck.

Swans mate for life
'cause they're truly love-struck.

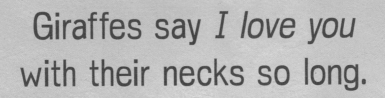

Giraffes say *I love you*
with their necks so long.

The nightingale sings
it in a beautiful song.

The peacock says *I love you*
with his feathers and flair.

Horses say *I love you*
by sharing their air.

Elephants hug
in their own
special way.

"I'm here, my dear"
is what they seem to say.

Lions say *I love you*
with a purr and a cuddle.

Wolves say *I love you*
with a howl and a huddle.

Bears like to say it
with a kiss on the muzzle.

A mama cow says it
with a lick and a nuzzle.

Mourning doves like
to bill and coo.
And that's how they
say *I love you.*

How Do Penguins Play?

Diane Muldrow

Illustrated by David Walker

Penguins like playing king of the hill!

Parrots will play
with a tweak on the bill.

Crows play
with sticks as
they fly through
the air . . .

and slide on their backs
in the snow, if they dare!

Breaching's big fun
for the humpback whale.

A woodpecker's toy
is another one's tail.

Dolphins blow bubbles,
then bounce them around.

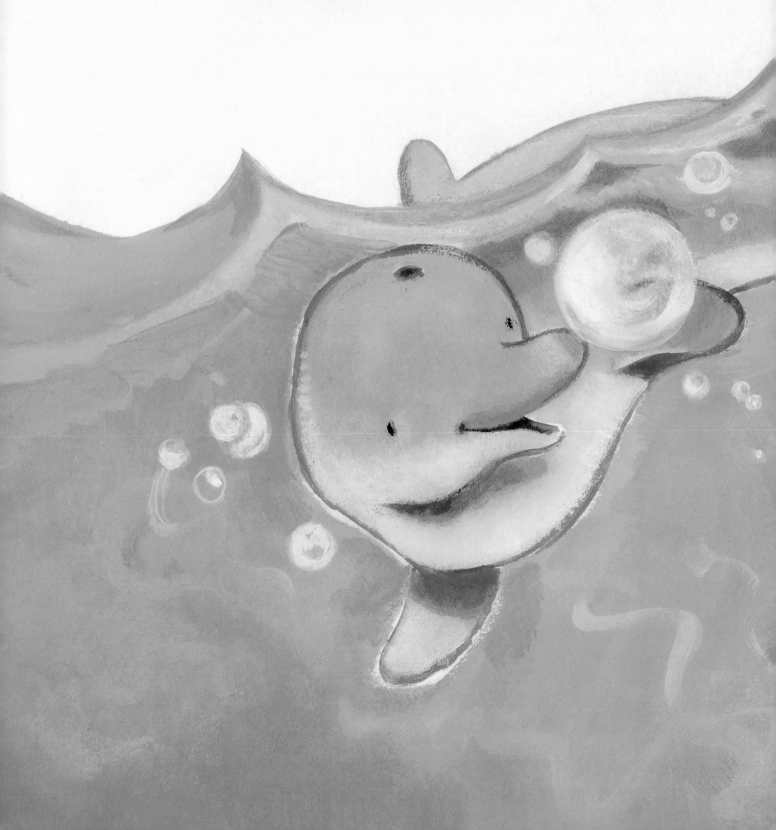

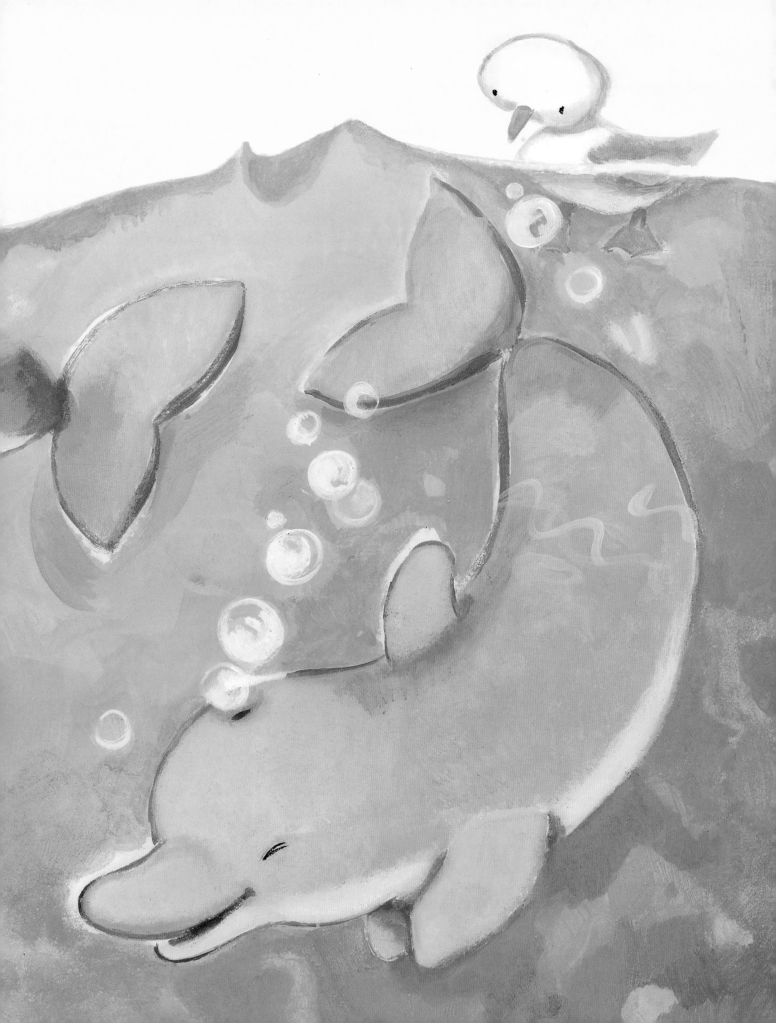

Grizzly cubs wrestle
their friends to the ground.

Monkeys flip . . .

and seals flop.

Kangaroos like to box
as they hop.

Young goats leap high
and kick up their heels!

Sea otters are allowed
to play with their meals!

Cheetahs pounce the whole day through.

Animals love to play—just like you!

How Do Giraffes Take Naps?

Diane Muldrow • Illustrated by David Walker

Puppies keep warm
when they sleep in a heap.

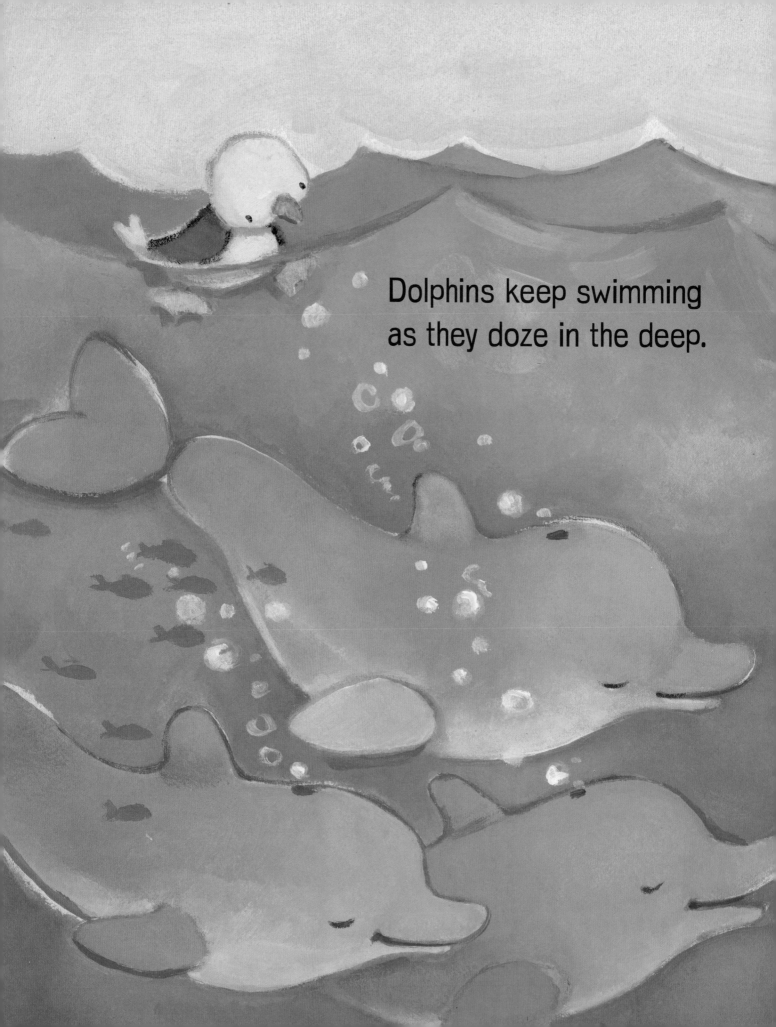

Dolphins keep swimming
as they doze in the deep.

Leopards can snooze
up high in a tree.

The giraffe's behind makes
a nice pillow, you see.

Frogs spend the winter asleep under ice!

Sloths think dozing
upside down is nice.

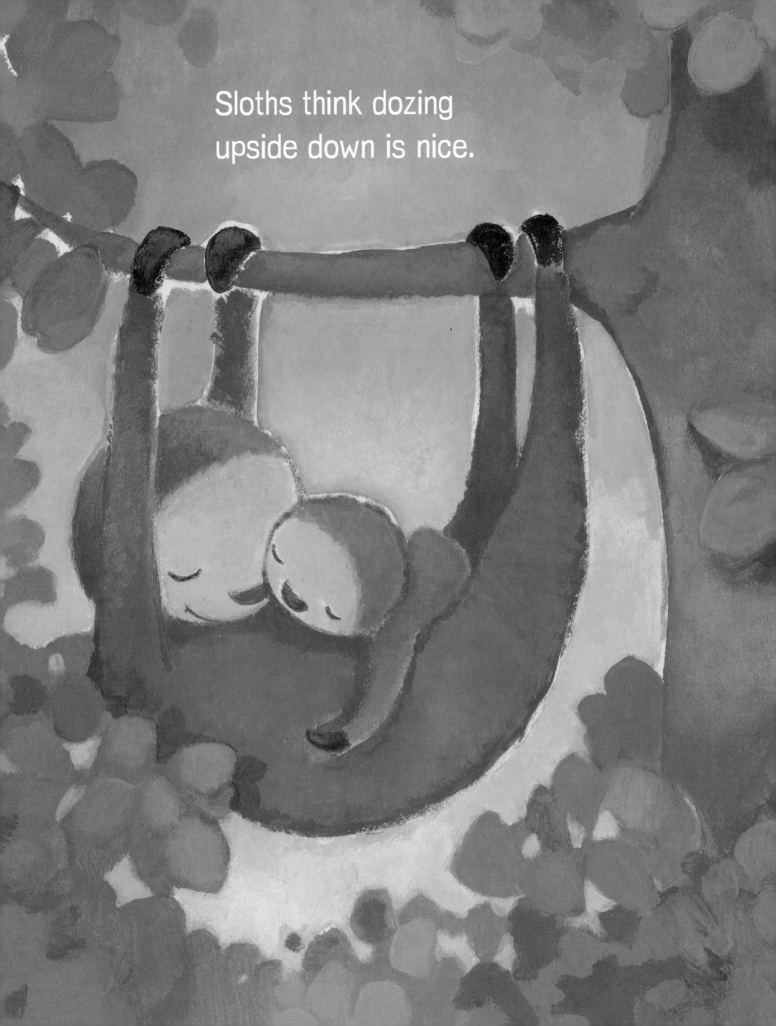

A bird likes to nap tucked under its wing.

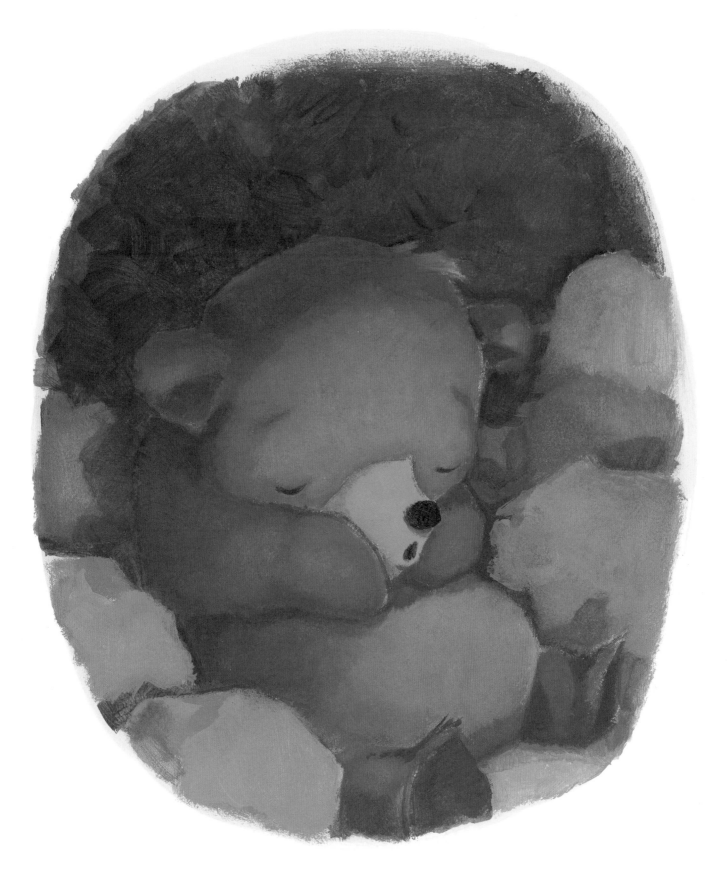

Bears hibernate from autumn till spring.

Sea otters sometimes sleep holding paws.

Crocodiles doze with wide-open jaws!

Lions laze around
in the shade all day.

House cats will nap *any* which way!

Koalas can sleep
for twelve hours
or more.

Elephants have been known to snore!

A horse can doze
standing up in its stall . . .

And some baby whales
don't sleep at all!

Gorillas cuddle and close their eyes tight.
Just like you, they sleep through the night!